SCHOLASTIC

W9-AYA-184
C

DRESS-UP
Day

by Mary Atkinson

Can you find
a ladybug on
every page?

make
believe
ideas

Some pets can fly.

Some pets can sing.

Some pets have glasses.

Some pets have wings.

Some pets are pirates.

Some pets are clowns.

Some pets wear hats.

Some pets wear crowns.

Some pets play ball.

Some pets read books.

Some pets can drive.

Some pets can cook.

Some pets wear yellow.

Some pets wear gray.

All pets are fun.

It's Dress-up Day!

Discussion Questions

1 Which pet is wearing a crown?

2 Which pet likes music?

3 What would you like to dress up as? Why?

SIGHT WORDS

Learning sight words helps you read fluently.
Practice these sight words from the book.
Use them in sentences of your own.

are   can

fly   play

sing

read   some